# THIS BOOK BELONGS TO:

## この本は

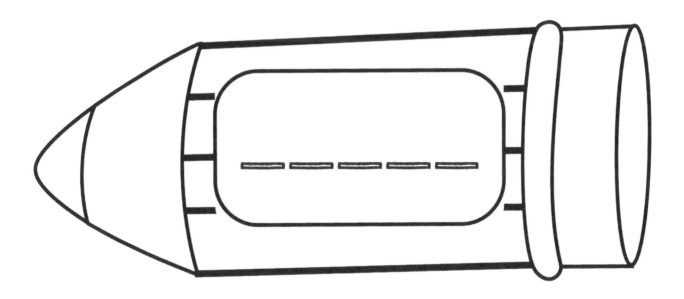

## のものだ

木 き

TREE        [ki]

SUN/DAY     [hi]

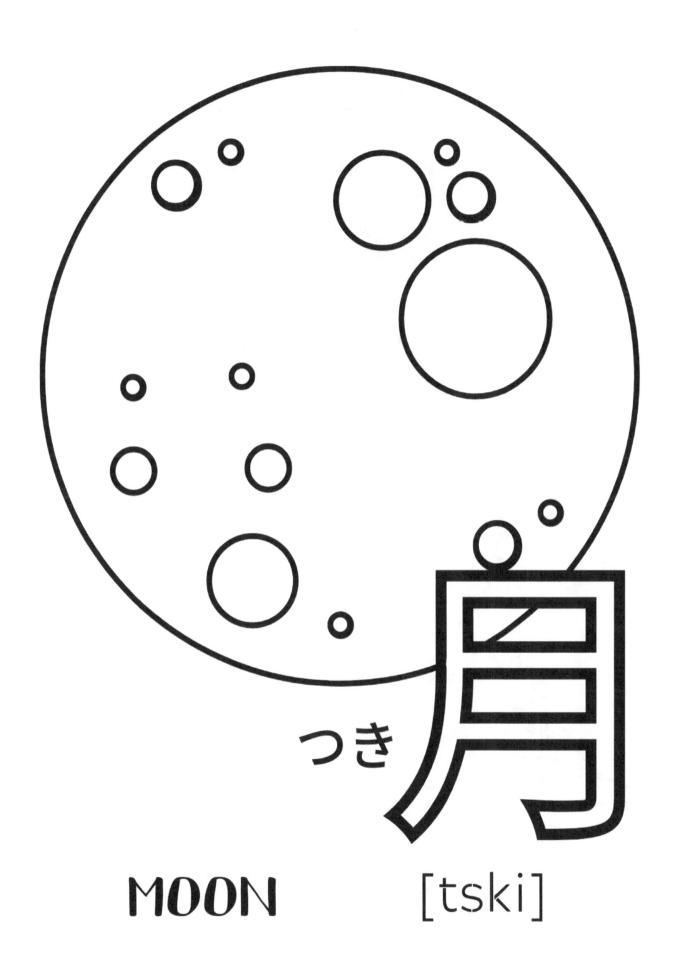

MOON　　　　[tski]

もり

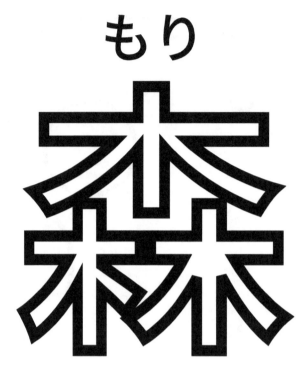

WOOD     [mori]

あめ

RAIN          [ame]

FIRE                    [hi]

ほん

本

BOOK          [hon]

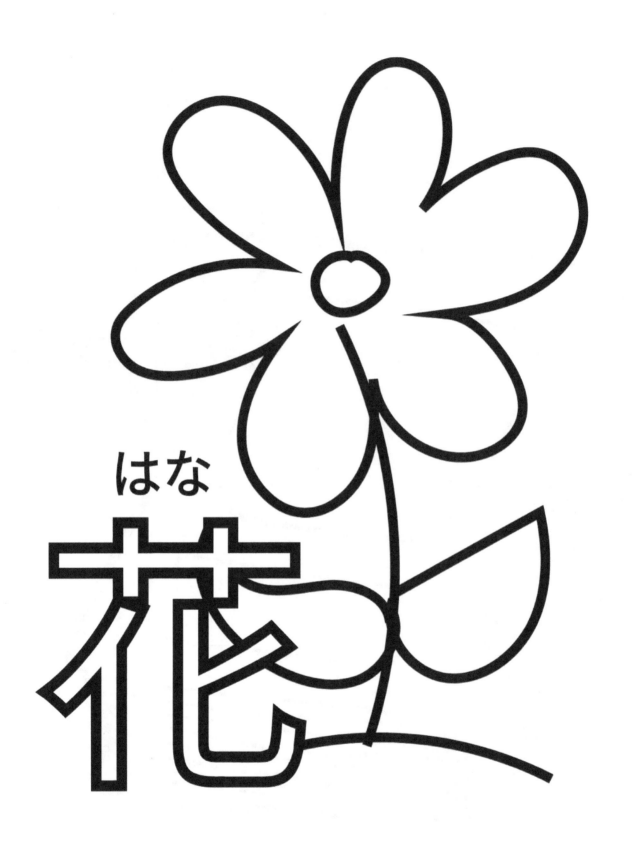

はな
花

FLOWER     [hana]

つち

EARTH/SOIL   [tsuchi]

いぬ

犬

DOG　　　[inu]

うま

馬

HORSE　　　[uma]

さかな

魚

FISH    [sakana]

とり

BIRD          [tori]

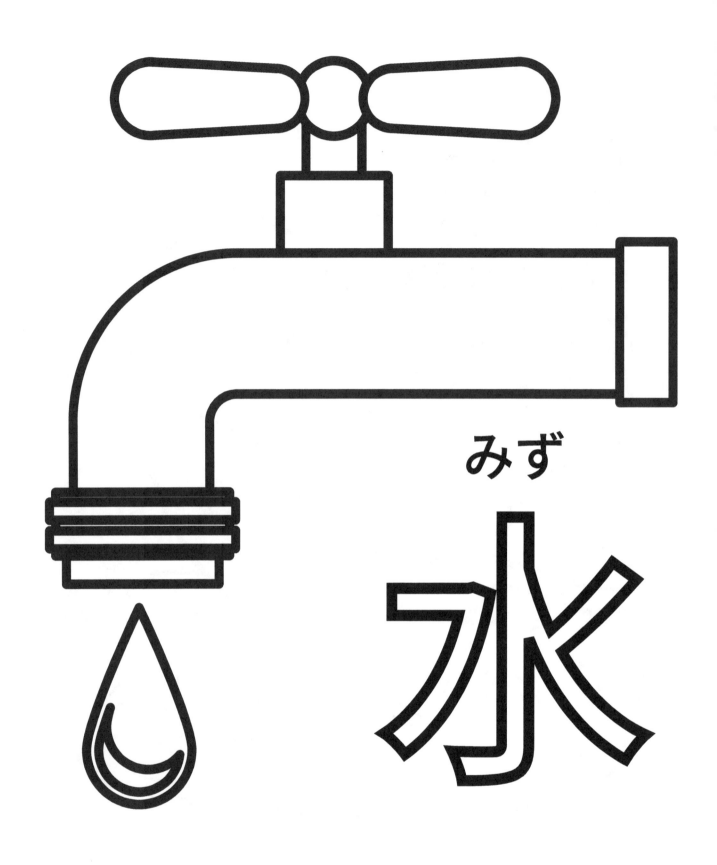

みず

水

WATER      [mizu]

かわ

川

RIVER     [kava]

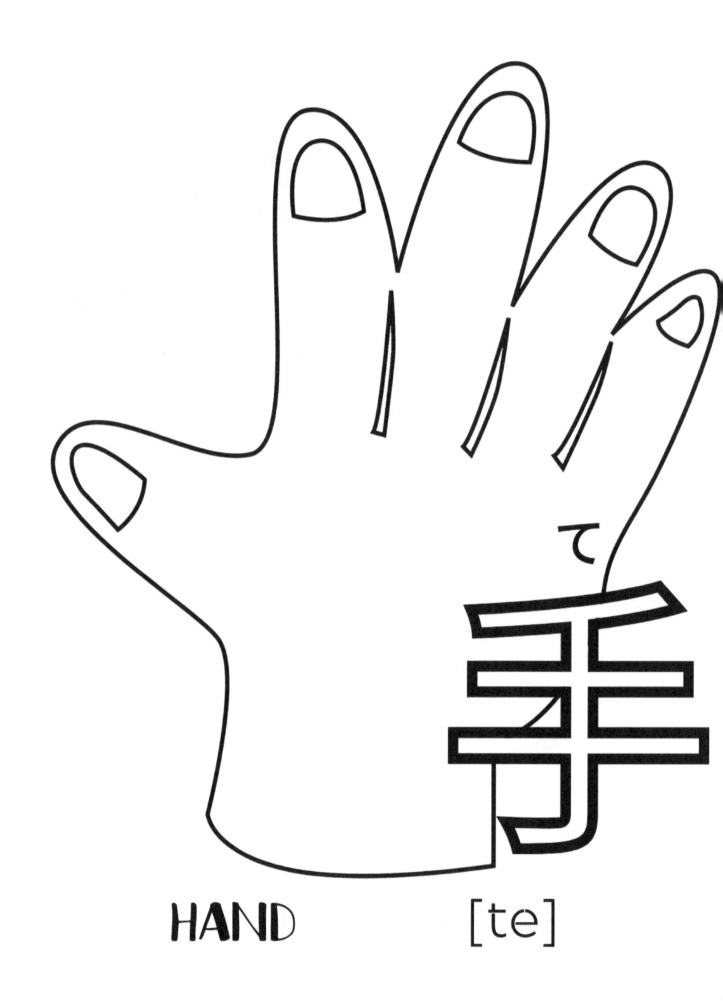

HAND          [te]

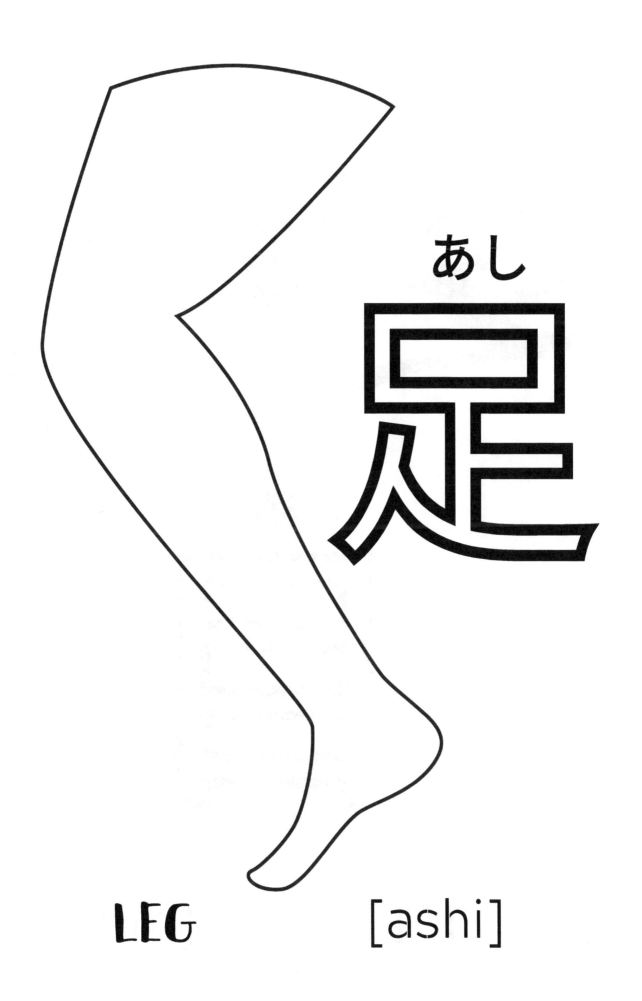

あし

足

LEG     [ashi]

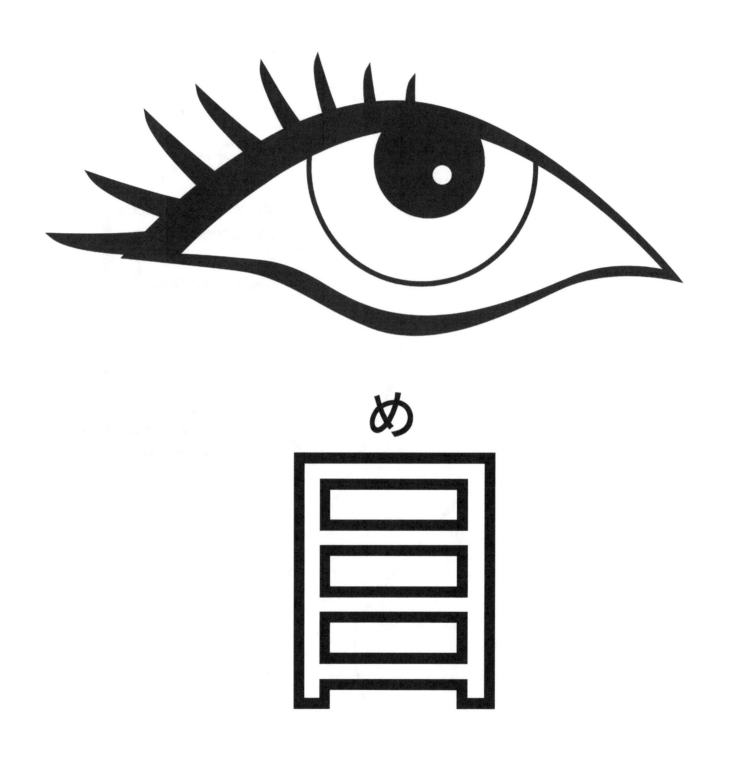

EYE        [me]

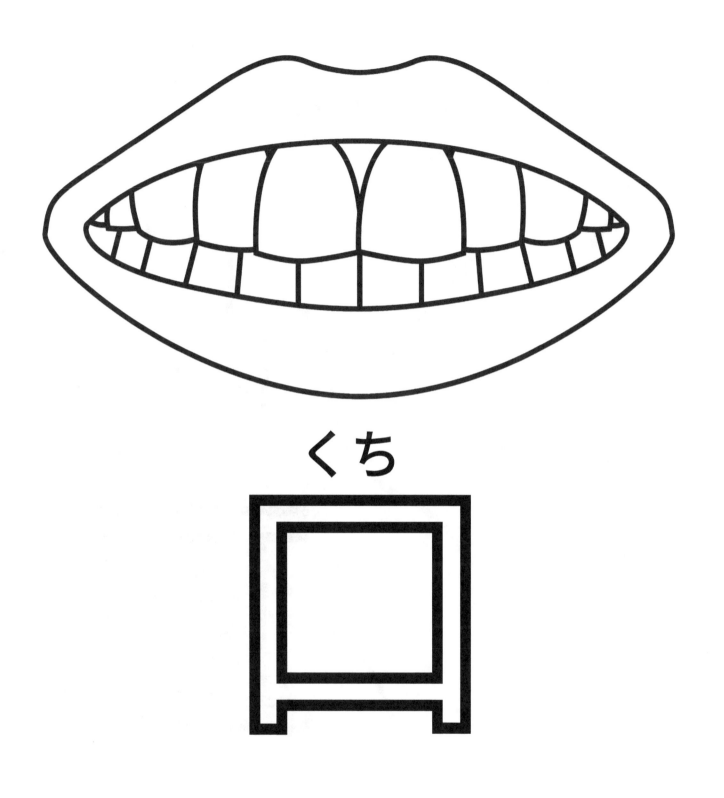

くち

MOUTH   [kuchi]

EAR        [mimi]

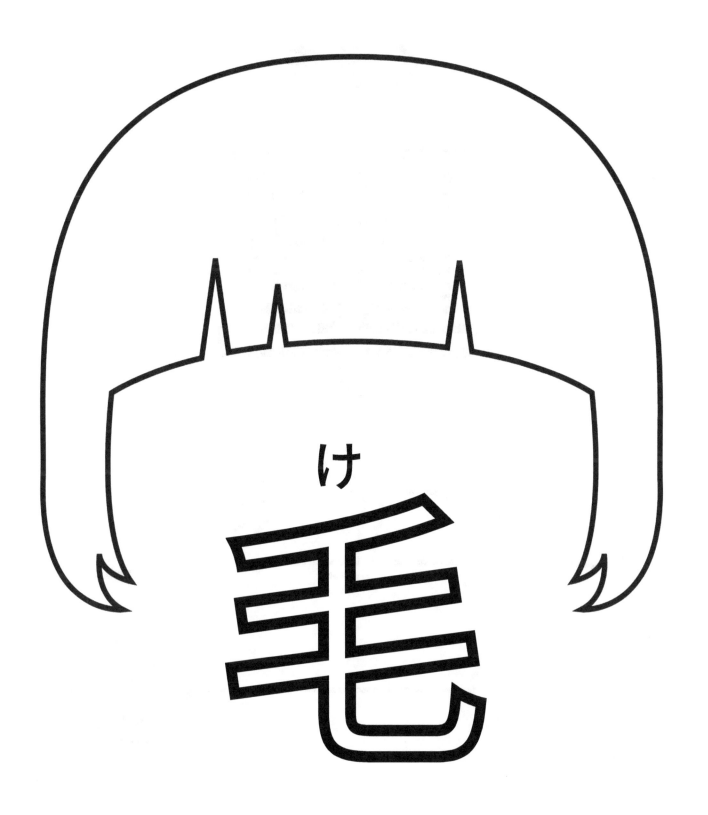

HAIR     [ke]

くるま

車

CAR [kuruma]

お金
かね

MONEY　　[okane]

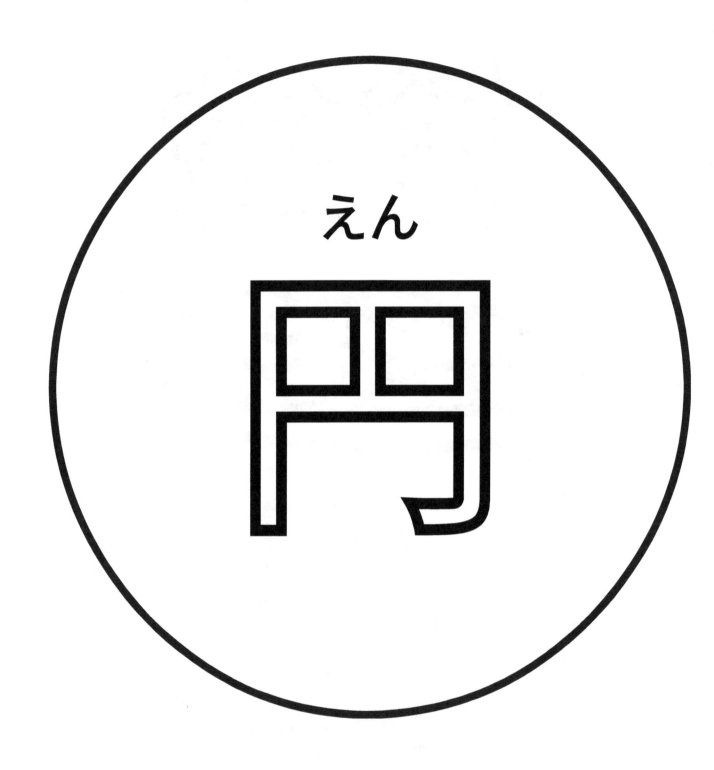

CIRCLE　　　[en]

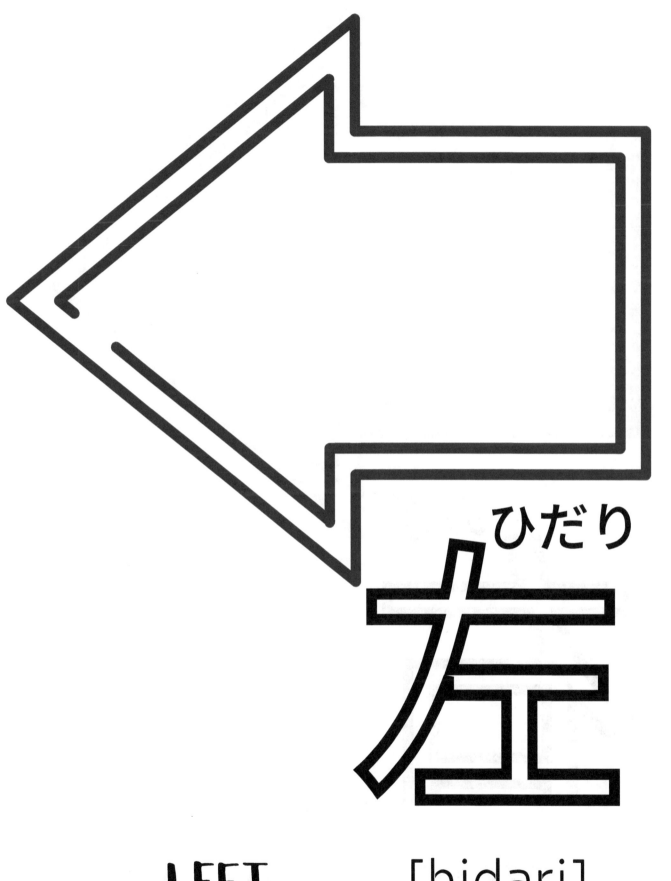

ひだり

左

LEFT　　　　[hidari]

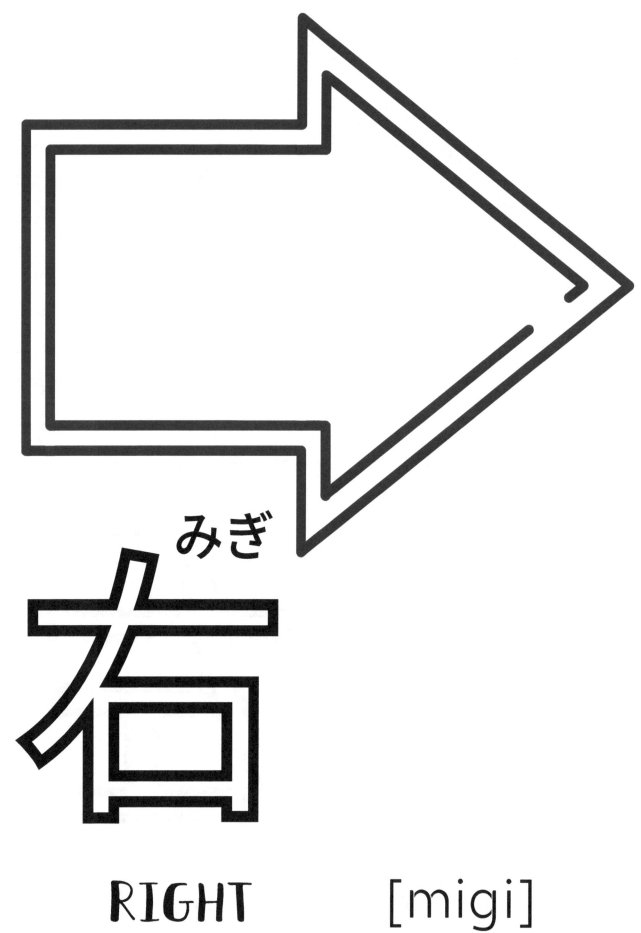

みぎ

右

RIGHT        [migi]

かい

SHELLFISH    [kai]

RICE    [gohan]

くに

COUNTRY     [kuni]

いち

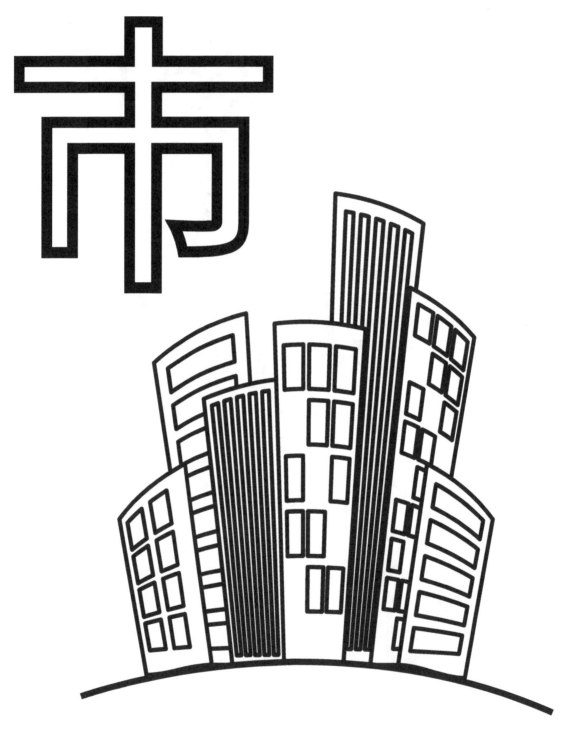

CITY                    [ichi]

みせ

SHOP    [mise]

こころ

心

HEART    [kokoro]

ひと

人

PERSON     [hito]

# お<ruby>父<rt>とう</rt></ruby>さん

FATHER    [otōsan]

はは

MOTHER　　[haha]

CHILD        [ko]

とも

# 友だち

FRIEND     [tomodachi]

おとこ

男

MAN          [otoko]

おんな

オ

WOMAN    [onna]

た
# 食べる

TO EAT     [taberu]

の

飲む

TO DRINK　[nomu]

た
立つ

TO STAND  [tatsu]

行く

TO GO  [iku]

# み
# 見る

TO WATCH    [miru]

TO TALK     [hanasu]

休む

TO REST　　[yasumu]

か

書く

TO WRITE    [kaku]

おも

思う

TO THINK  [omou]

か
買う

TO BUY          [kau]

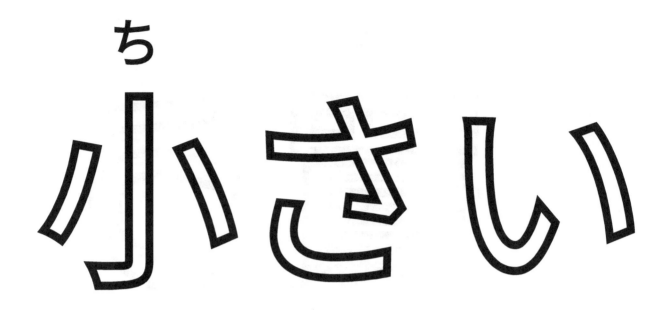

**SMALL** [chīsai]

おう
大きい

BIG          [ōkī]

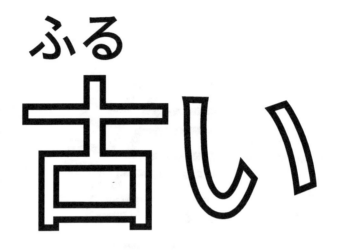

OLD     [furui]

たか
# 高い

HIGH [takai]

でん
# 電き

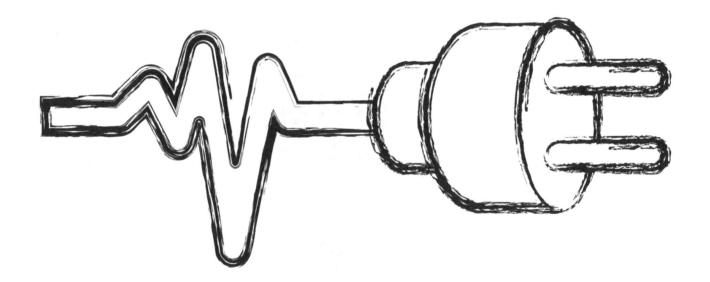

ELECTRICITY　　[denki]

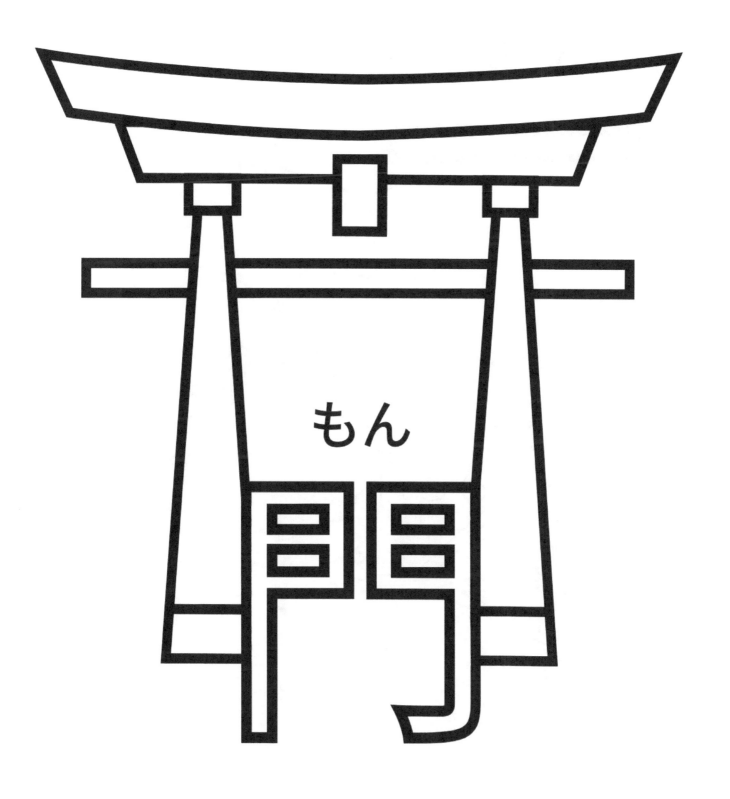

もん

GATES     [mon]

いち

一

ONE          [ichi]

に

TWO          [ni]

さん

三

THREE          [san]

し

四

FOUR     [shi]

FIVE          [go]

ろく

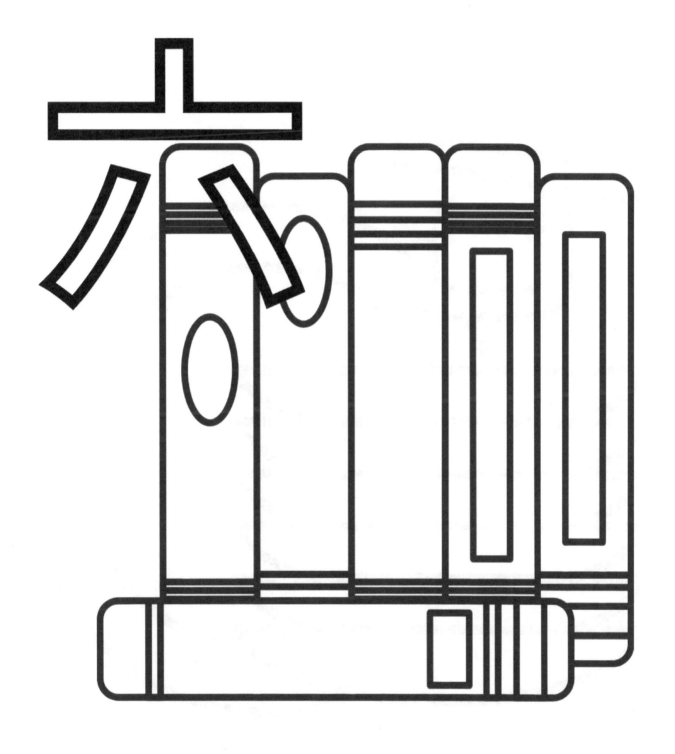

SIX          [roku]

しち

SEVEN [shichi]

はち

八

EIGHT     [hachi]

きゅう

九

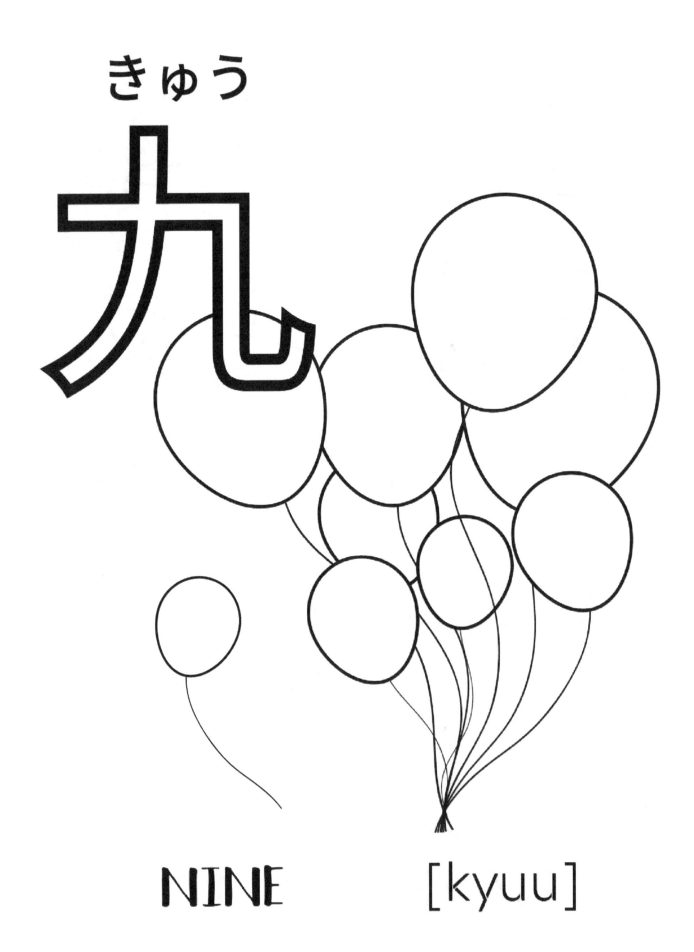

NINE    [kyuu]

じゅう

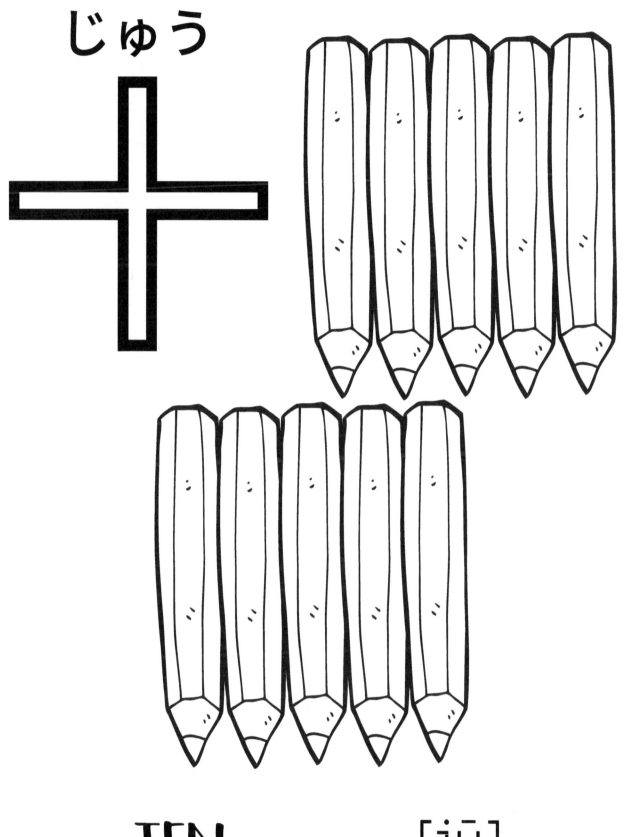

TEN          [jū]

Made in United States
Troutdale, OR
11/03/2024

24421354R00038